Addition to Five

Written by Sue Lambert and Sandi Rickerby

Published by World Teachers Press®

Printed in the United States of America.

This book is printed on recycled paper.

Order Number 2-5099
ISBN 978-1-58324-021-2

H I J K L 14 13 12 11 10

The Association of Educational Publishers

395 Main Street
Rowley, MA 01969
www.didax.com

Foreword

The *Early Skills Series* of books is designed to give students practice in a range of early reading, writing and number activities as well as to develop perceptual and fine motor skills in the early years.

Early Skills Series – Addition to Five contains activities enabling students to practice writing, counting and adding numerals to five.

The worksheets can be used to motivate students to work independently, increase their concentration span and develop their ability to work in an orderly fashion; encouraging them to take pride in the presentation of their work at the same time.

The worksheets are bold, uncluttered and visually appealing to young students. They contain instruction in graphic form, thereby requiring minimum support from you. They can be used to teach a new skill or to reinforce and consolidate those already taught.

Other books in this series are:

Early Skills Series – Counting and Recognition to Five
Early Skills Series – Early Visual Skills
Early Skills Series – Cutting Activities

Contents

Teacher Information

Introduction

Development of perceptual and fine motor skills in the early years is extremely important if students are to have a good grounding to progress to the next level of development. The *Early Skills Series* is designed to give practice in the aforementioned areas in a range of early reading, writing and numerical areas of the curriculum.

The worksheets are motivational and designed to encourage students to work independently wherever possible. This encourages high self-esteem, increases concentration span and develops the ability to work in a logical and orderly fashion.

The clear layout of each worksheet allows the student to concentrate solely on the task at hand. The large, open artwork appeals to students and has been drawn at the appropriate level for students' fine motor skill development.

Suggested Implementation

The *Early Skills Series* can be implemented easily into any existing program.

1. Familiarize students with the icons on page 6. This page could be enlarged and colored and displayed in a prominent position within the classroom. Students can then refer to the icons whenever they need to.
2. Develop recognition and understanding of the key words shown on the worksheets. Students may learn to read these words as sight words. This will help develop their independence in completing the worksheet.
3. Discuss and explain each worksheet after all students have their worksheet in front of them.
   (a) Students sit on the mat area. You have an enlarged version of the worksheet.
   (b) Discuss the icons at the top of the page. Students can offer you the instructions for the page.
   (c) Work through the page, showing the students the completed product.
   (d) Students move back to their own work area to complete the worksheet independently.
4. Worksheets can be collected and viewed to determine areas of need for each student or the whole class group.

Teacher Information

Instructions

The instructions provided on each worksheet are in graphic form, thereby requiring minimal support from you. A key explaining each graphic is located on page six.

Benefits

The benefits of the *Early Skills Series* are many.

1. You can readily evaluate where each student is having success or difficulty.
2. Students are provided with the opportunity to work independently.
3. Children develop perceptual and fine motor skills in the areas of early reading, writing and numbers.
4. Students to become familiar with a general range of instructional text.
5. Students are able to develop logic and to work in an orderly fashion.
6. The worksheets are highly motivational.
7. The program is easy to implement into any classroom.

Conclusion

The *Early Skills Series* provides worksheets to cover Early Visual Skills, Cutting, Counting and Recognition to Five and Addition to Five; areas which are of major significance in the students' development in the early years of education. A solid grounding in these areas ensures smooth progression onto the next level of development. The activities are designed to allow the students to experience success, developing confidence and a positive self-image toward themselves as a learner. A positive self-image is important if students are to experiment in their learning process without fear of failure.

Key - Addition to Five

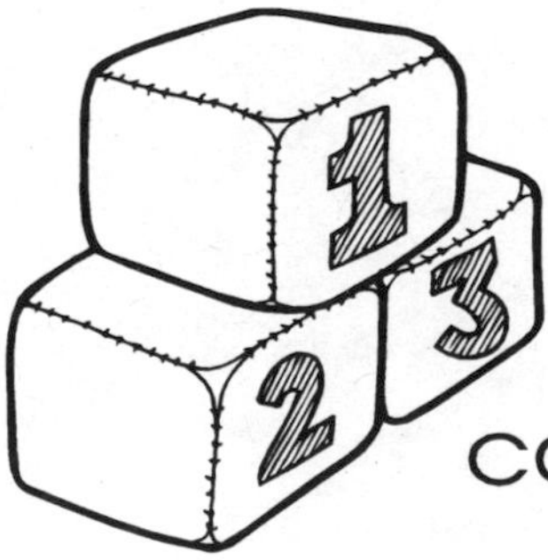 count	Count the pictures or numbers.
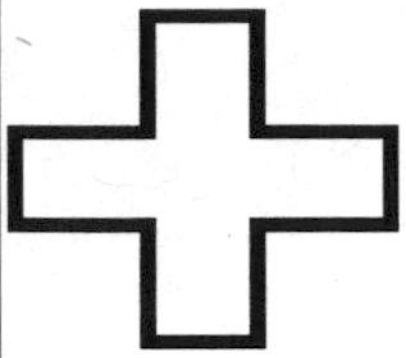 add	Add the numbers.
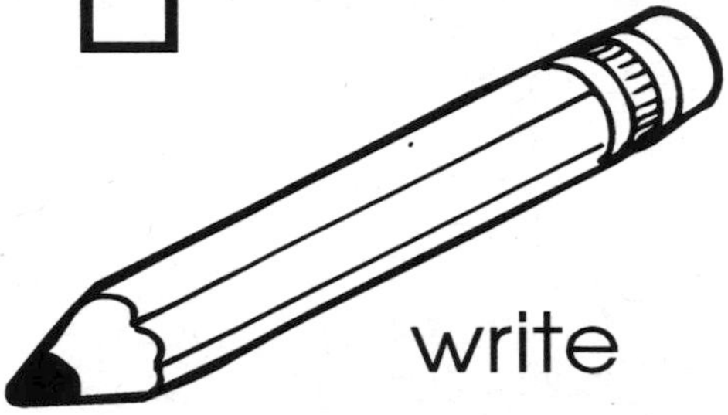 write	Write the answer.
color 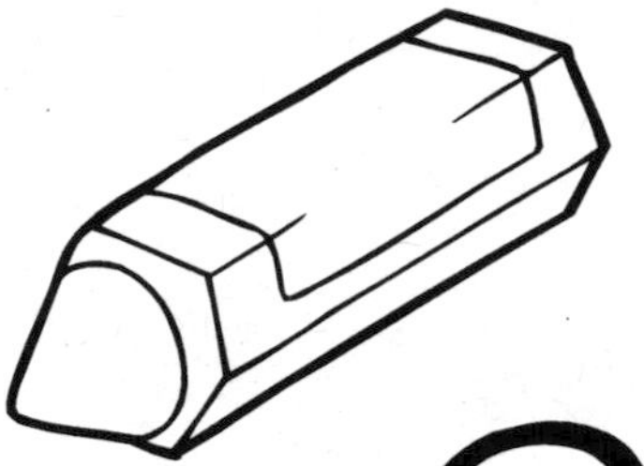	Color the pictures.
cut 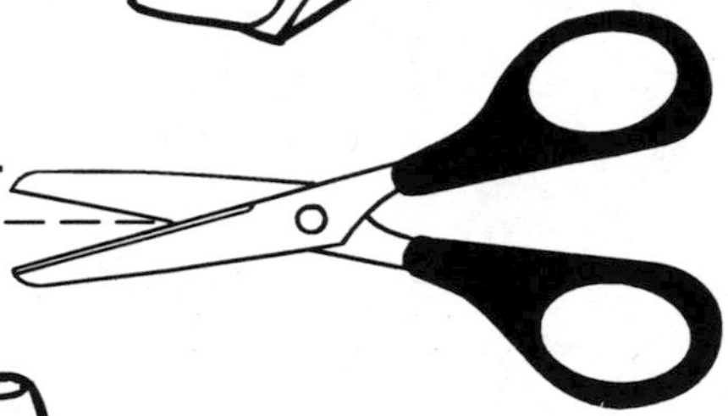	Cut along the dotted lines.
 glue	Glue into the correct place.
 draw	Draw the picture(s) as shown.

Name: ______________________ Date: ________________

1.  count 2.  write 3.  color

3 + 1 = 4

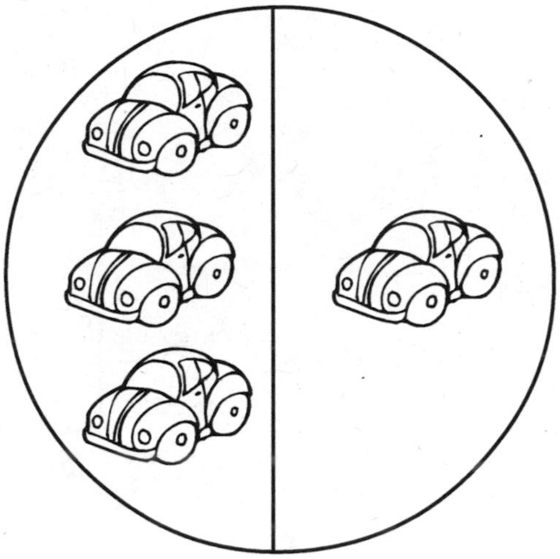

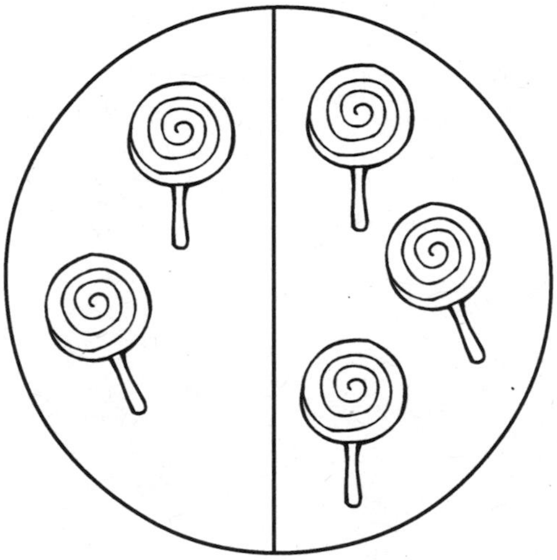

____ + ____ = ☐

____ + ____ = ☐

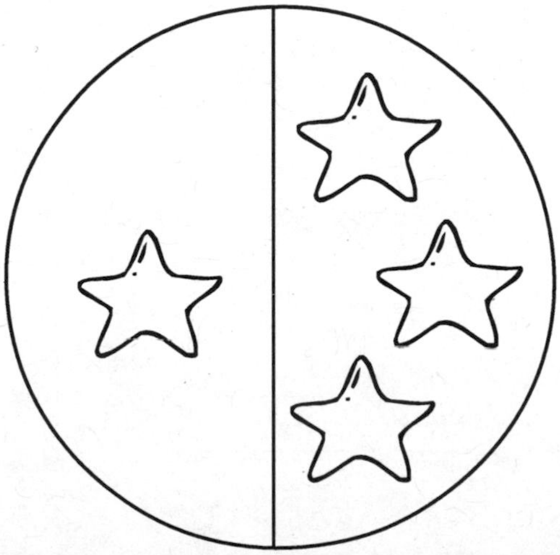

Name: ______________________________ Date: ____________________

1.  count 2.  write 3.  color

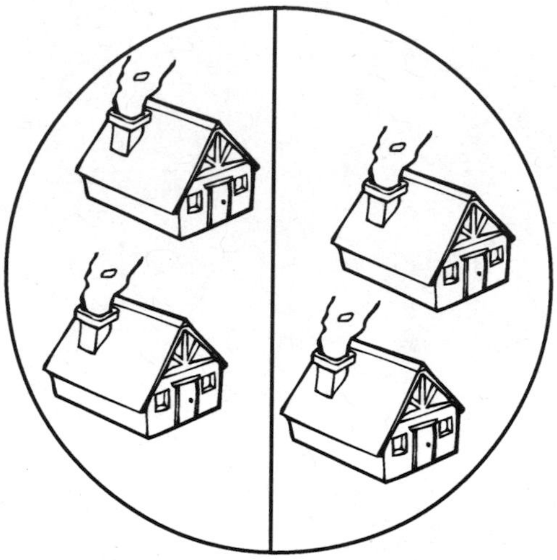

______ + ______ = ☐

______ + ______ = ☐

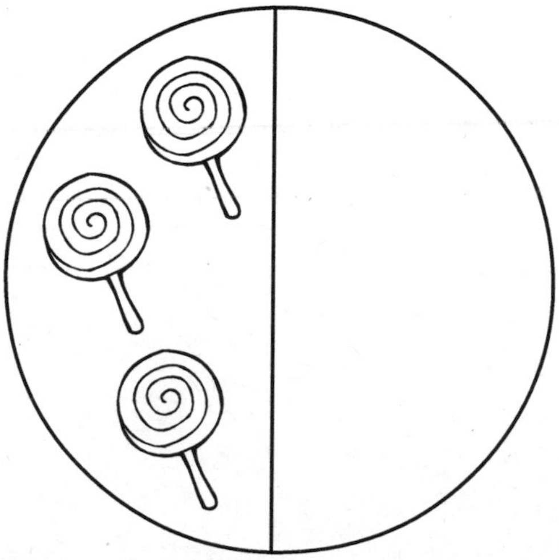

______ + ______ = ☐

Name: ______________________ Date: ______________

1.  count 2.  write 3. 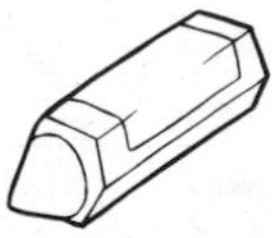 color

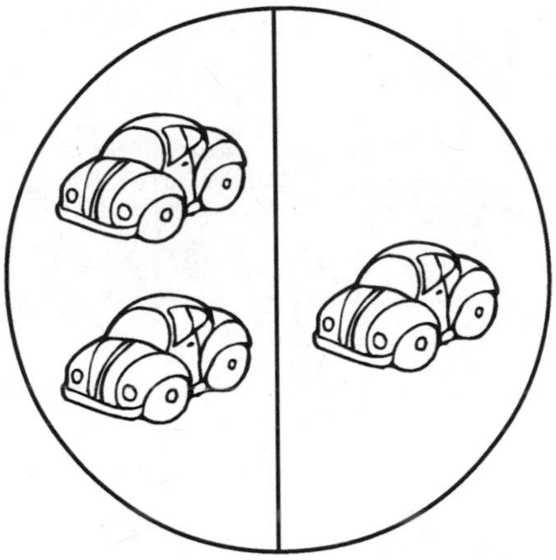

_____ + _____ = ☐

_____ + _____ = ☐

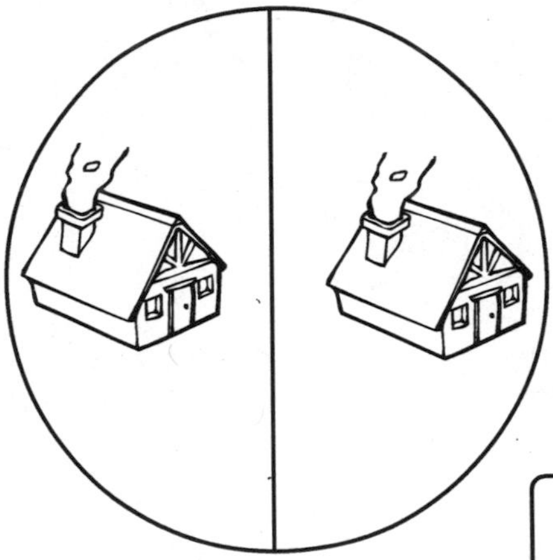

_____ + _____ = ☐

_____ + _____ = ☐

Name: ______________________ Date: ______________

1.  count 2.  write 3. 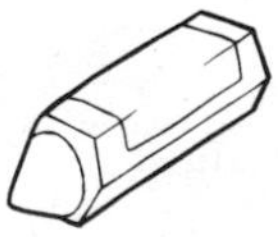 color

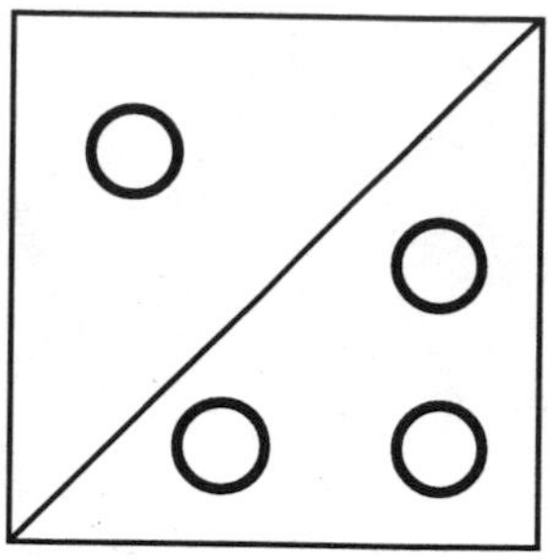

1 + 3 = 4

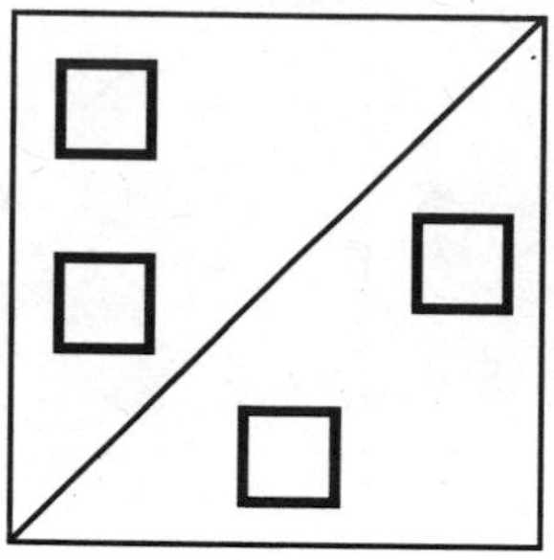

_____ + _____ = ☐

_____ + _____ = ☐

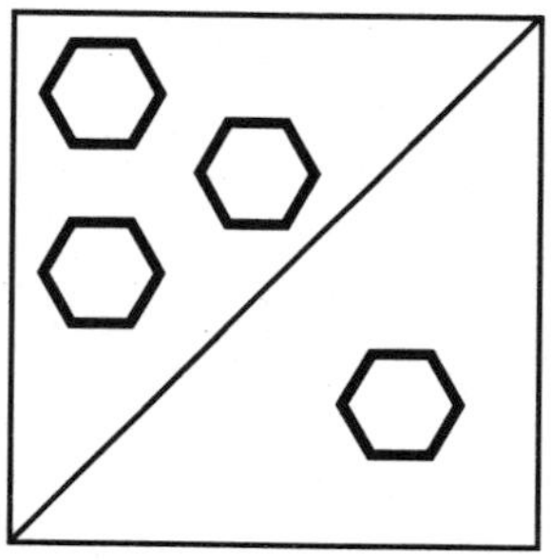

_____ + _____ = ☐

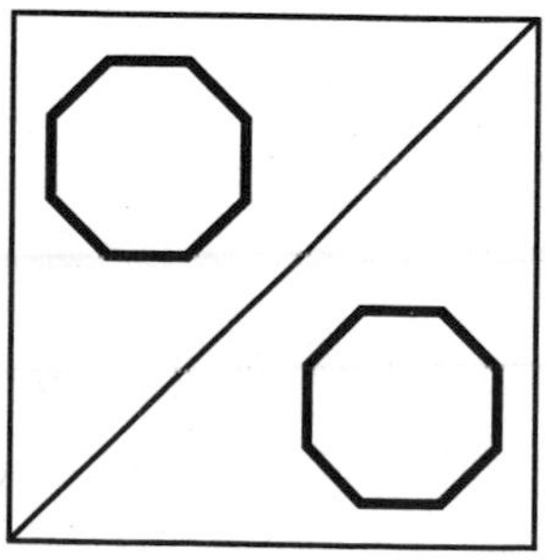

_____ + _____ = ☐

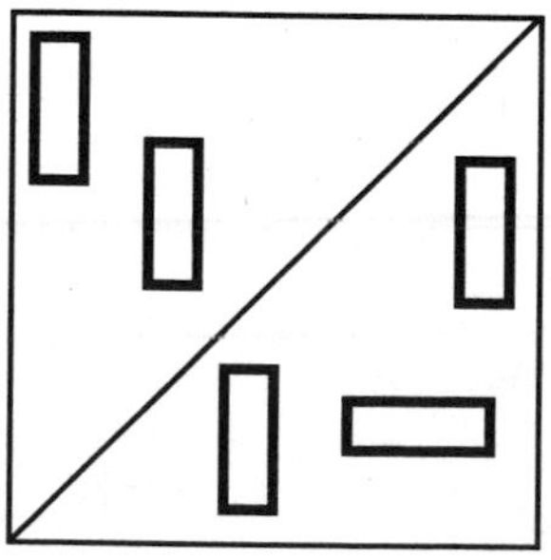

_____ + _____ = ☐

Name: ______________________________ Date: ____________________

1.  count 2.  write 3. 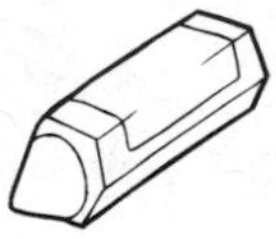 color

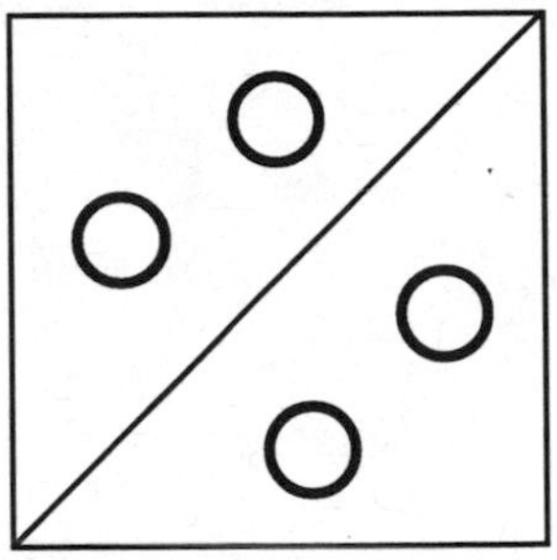

_____ + _____ = ☐

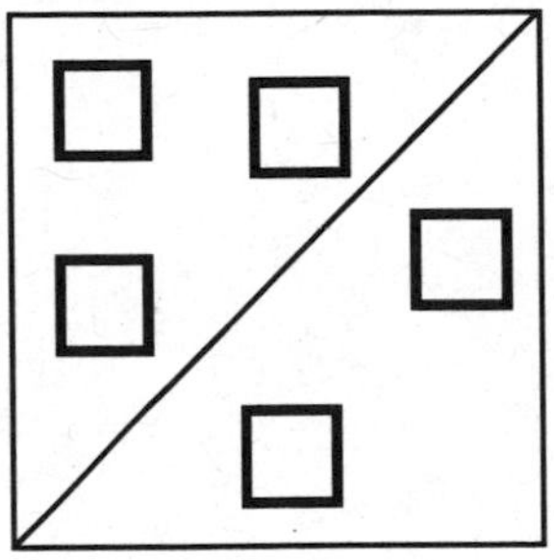

_____ + _____ = ☐

_____ + _____ = ☐

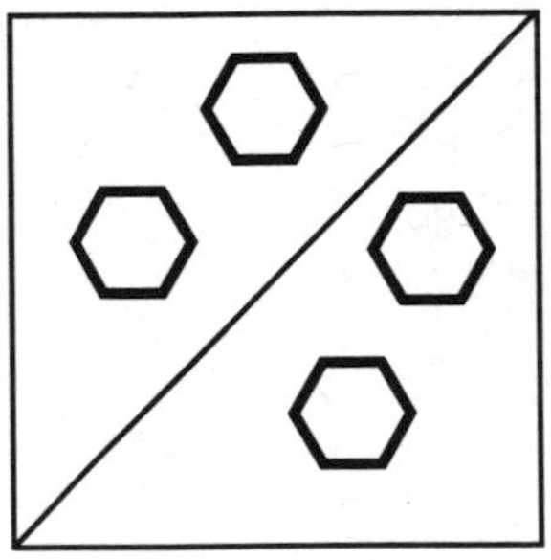

_____ + _____ = ☐

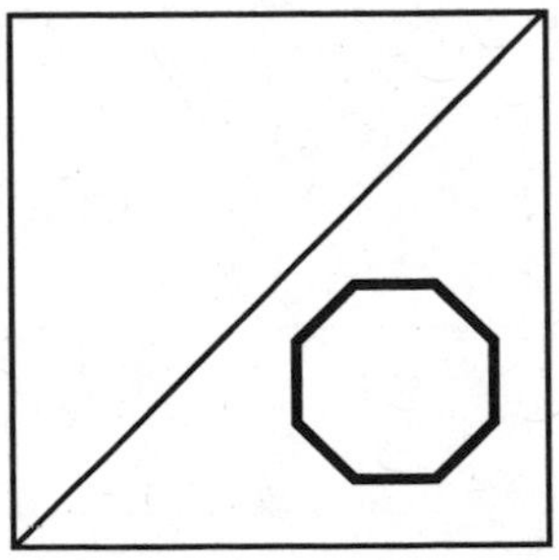

_____ + _____ = ☐

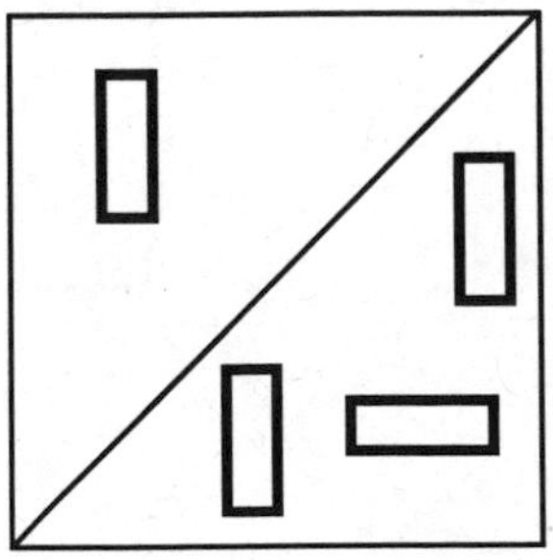

_____ + _____ = ☐

Name: ______________________________ Date: ____________________

1.  count 2. 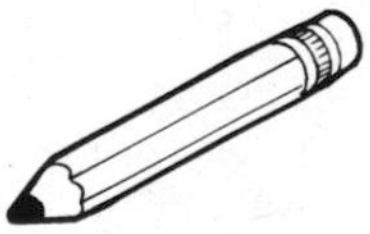 write 3. 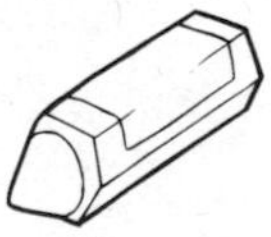 color

1 + 2 = 3

☐ + ☐ = ☐

 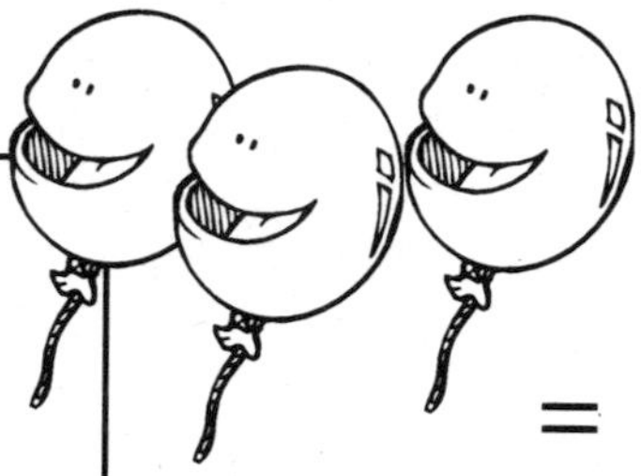

☐ + ☐ = ☐

☐ + ☐ = ☐

☐ + ☐ = ☐

Name: ______________________ Date: ______________________

1.  count **2.** 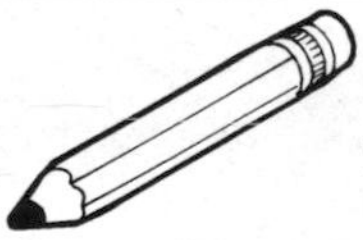 write **3.** 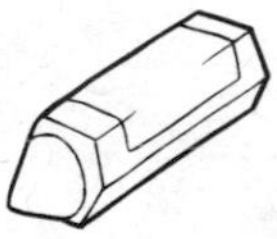 color

 +  =

 +  =

 +  =

 +  =

 +  =

Name: ______________________ Date: ____________

1.  count 2.  write 3. 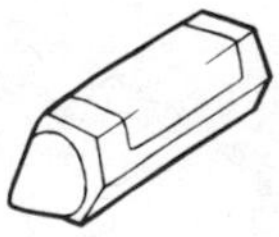 color

 +  =

 +  =

 +  =

 +  =

 +  =

Name: ______________________ Date: ______________

1. 

count

2. 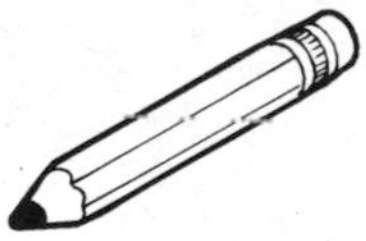 write

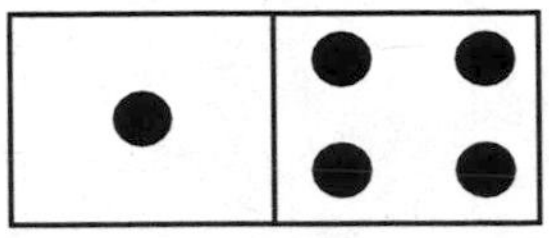
1 + 4 =

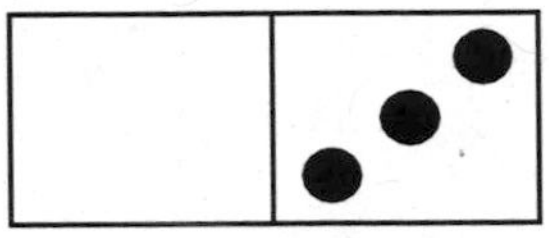
0 + 3 =

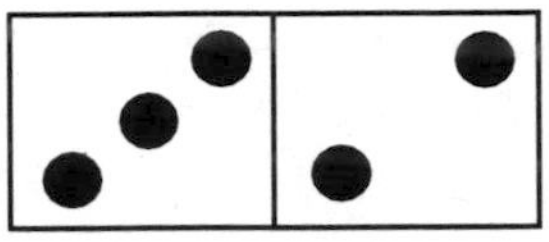
3 + 2 =

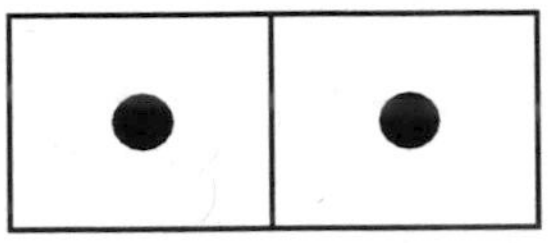
1 + 1 =

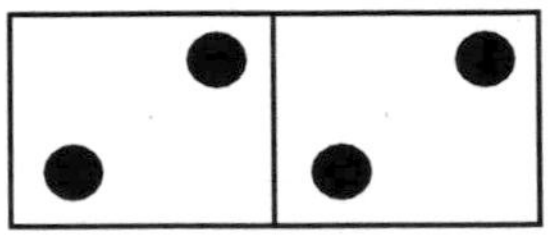
2 + 2 =

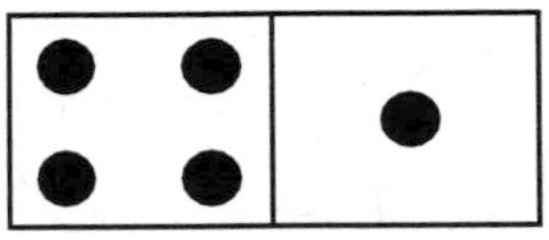
4 + 1 =

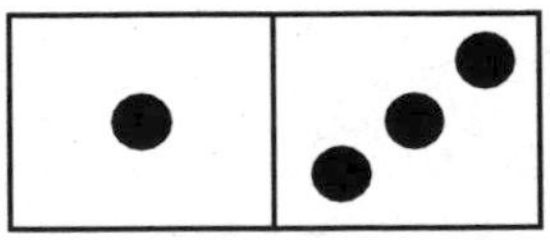
1 + 3 =

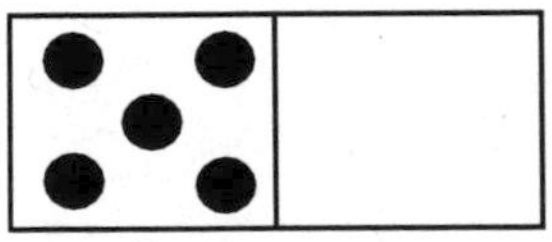
5 + 0 =

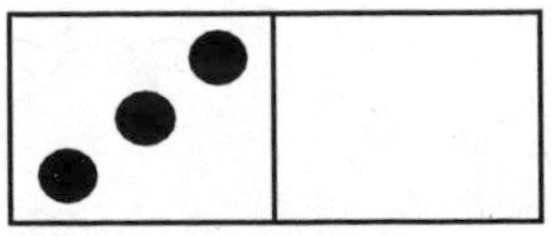
3 + 0 =

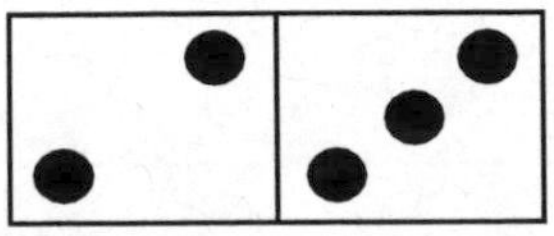
2 + 3 =

Name: ______________________ Date: ______________

1.  count **2.** 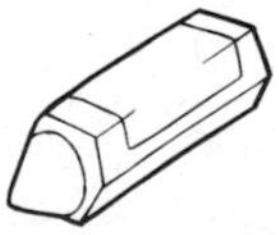 color **3.** 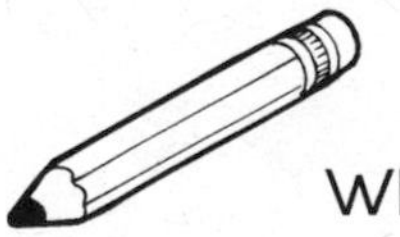 write

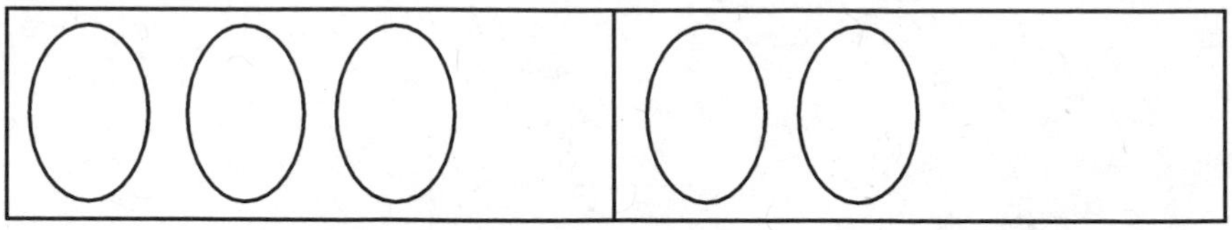

3 + 2 = 5

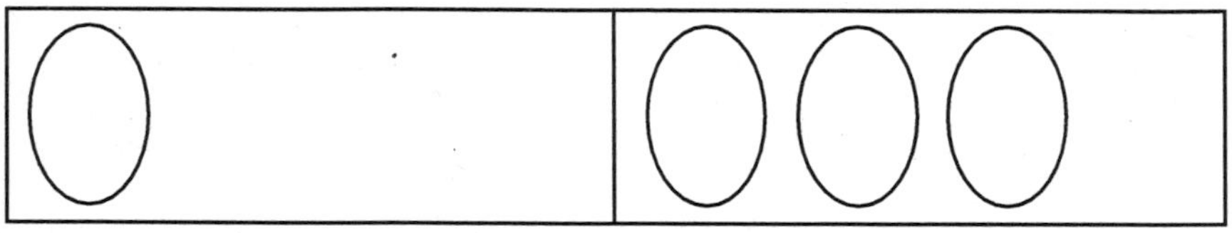

1 + 3 =

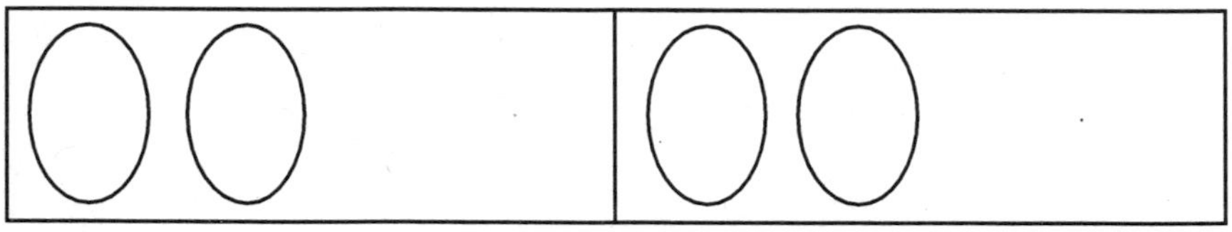

2 + 2 =

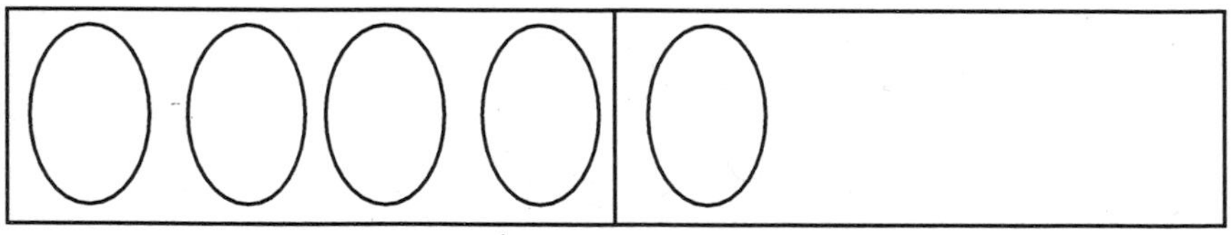

4 + 1 =

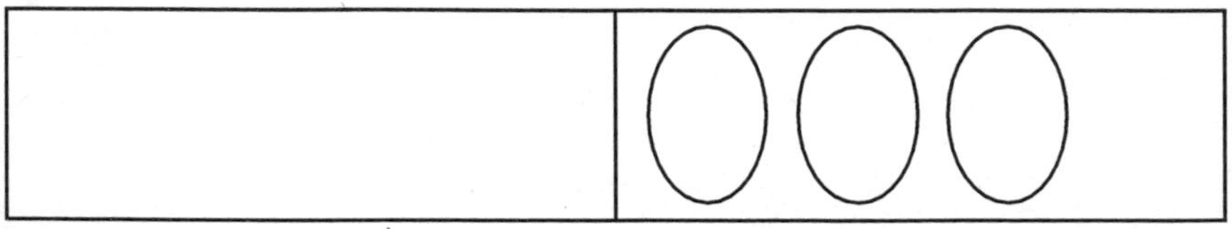

0 + 3 =

Name: ______________________ Date: ______________

1.  count **2.** 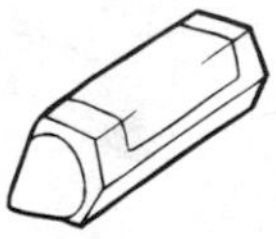 color **3.**  write

1 + 3 =

2 + 1 =

1 + 4 =

4 + 0 =

1 + 1 =

Name: ______________________ Date: ______________

1.  count **2.** 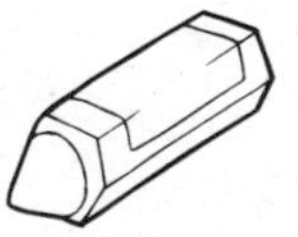 color **3.** 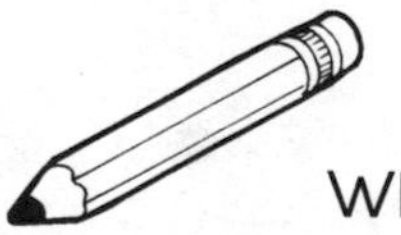 write

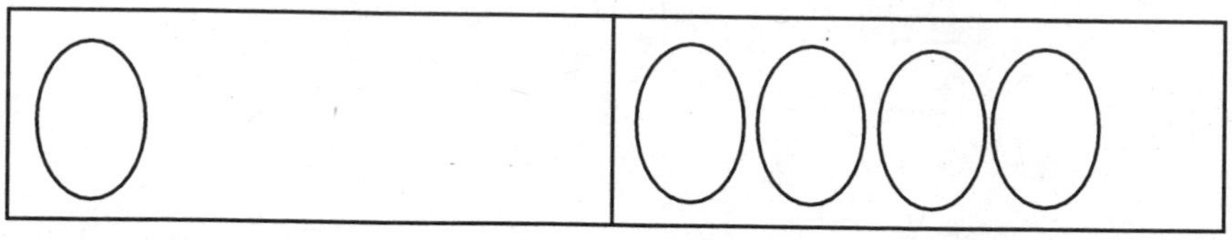

1 + 4 =

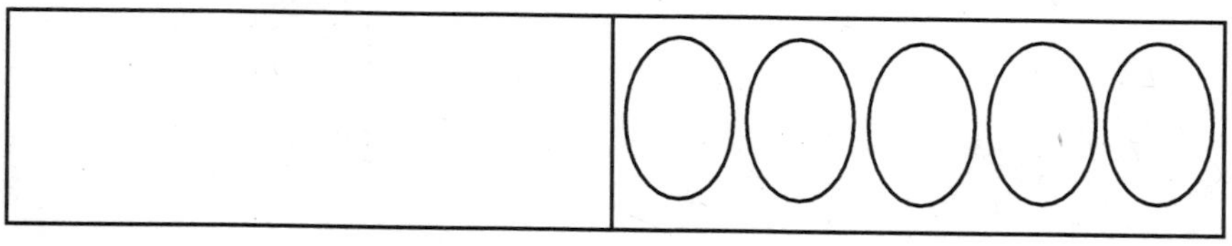

0 + 5 =

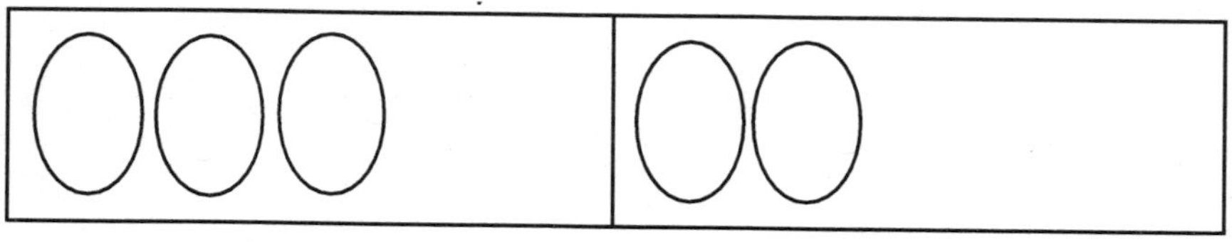

3 + 2 =

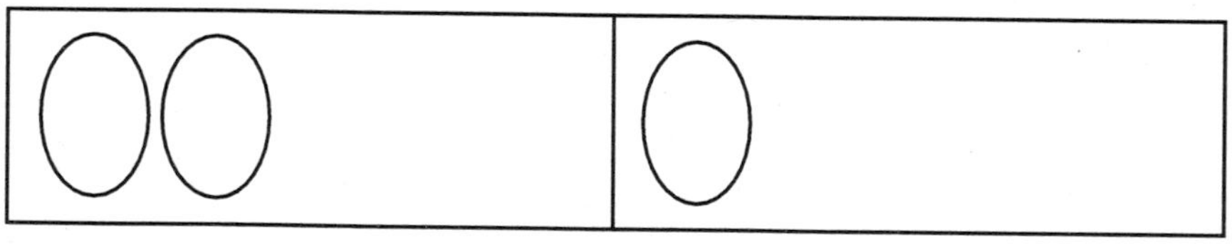

2 + 1 =

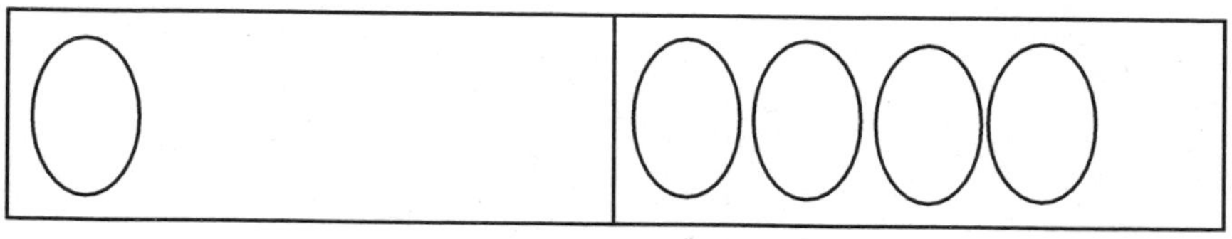

1 + 4 =

Name: ____________________ Date: ____________________

1.  count 2. 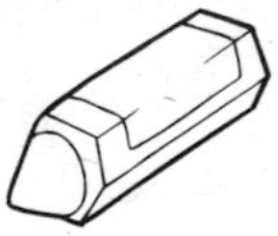 color 3.  write

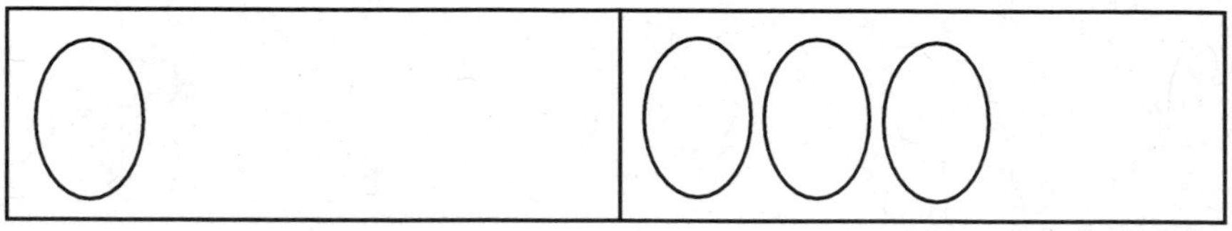

1 + 3 = ☐

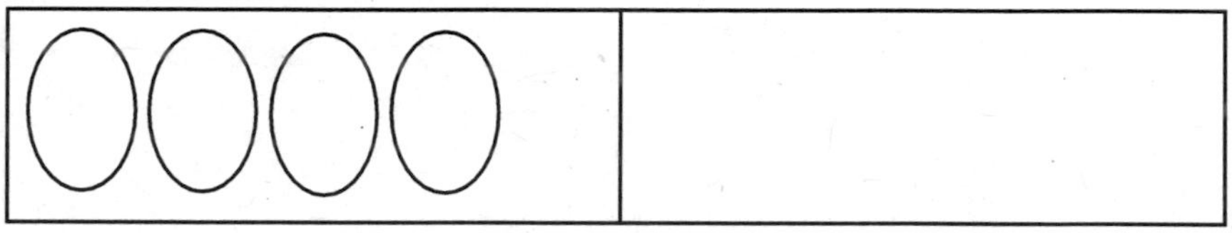

4 + 0 = ☐

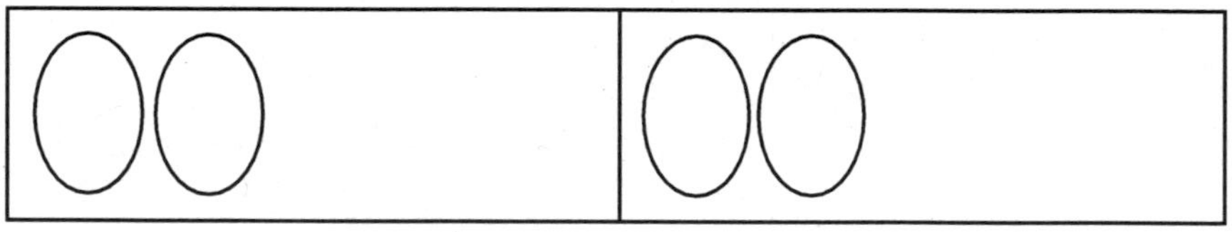

2 + 2 = ☐

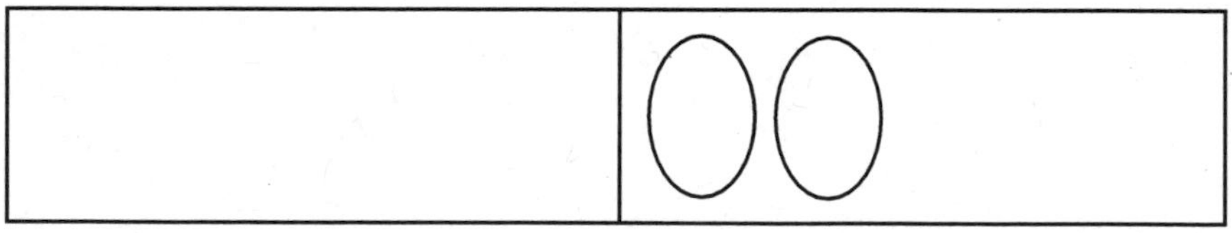

0 + 2 = ☐

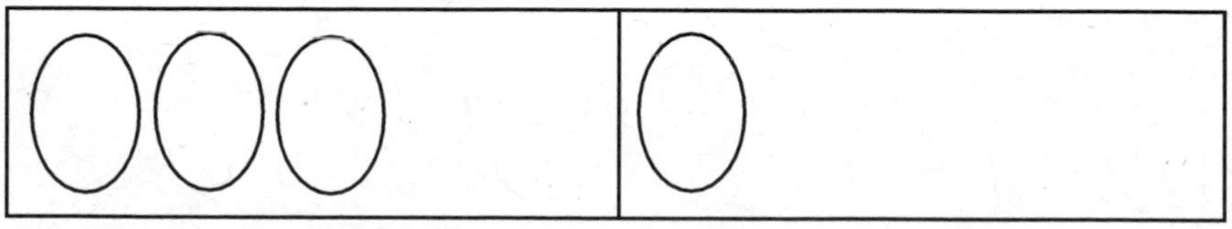

3 + 1 = ☐

Name: ______________________________ Date: ____________________

1.  count **2.** 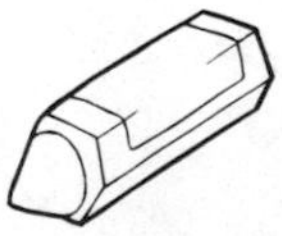 color **3.** 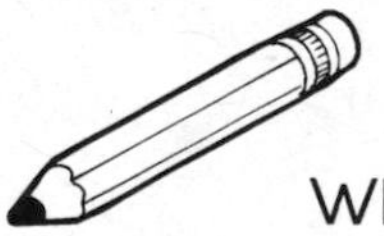 write

$3 + 2 = $ 5

$4 + 0 = $

$2 + 2 = $

$1 + 3 = $

$0 + 5 = $

Name: ______________________ Date: ______________

1. 

count

2. 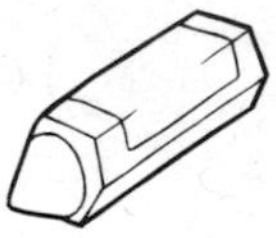
color

3. 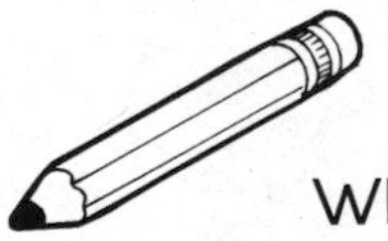
write

☐☐☐☐☐ + ☐☐☐☐☐ 2 + 3 = ☐

☐☐☐☐☐ + ☐☐☐☐☐ 3 + 1 = ☐

☐☐☐☐☐ + ☐☐☐☐☐ 1 + 2 = ☐

☐☐☐☐☐ + ☐☐☐☐☐ 4 + 1 = ☐

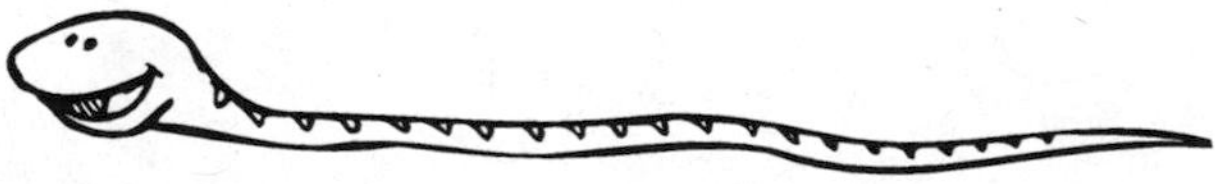

☐☐☐☐☐ + ☐☐☐☐☐ 2 + 2 = ☐

Name: ______________________ Date: ________________

1.  count **2.** 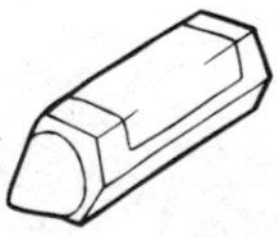 color **3.** 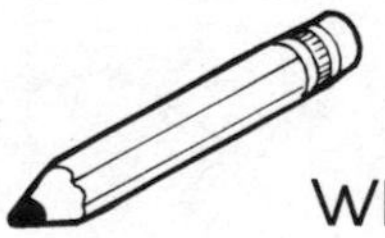 write

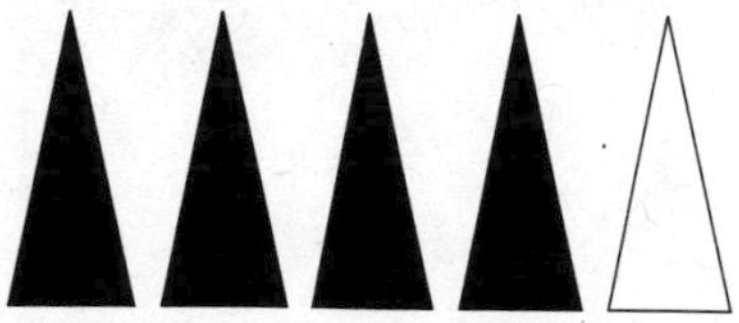 + 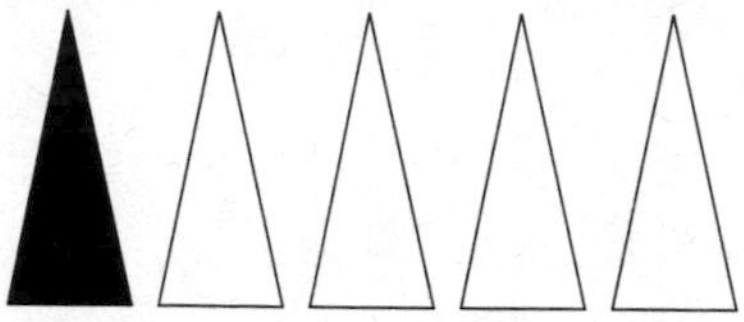 4 + 1 = **5**

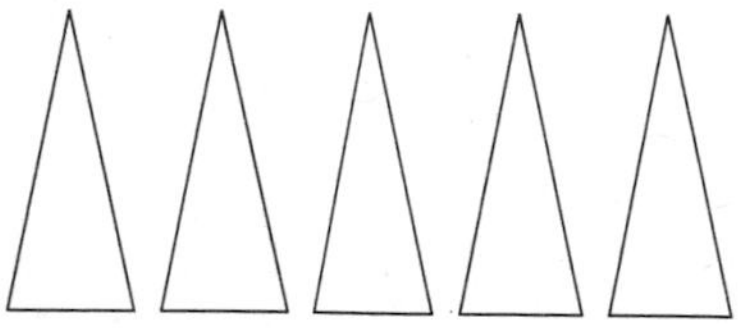 + 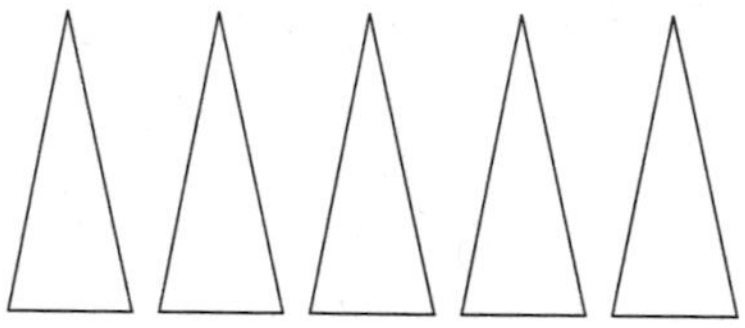 5 + 0 = ☐

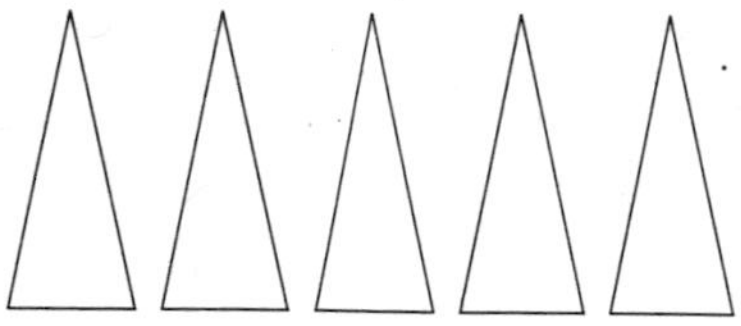 + 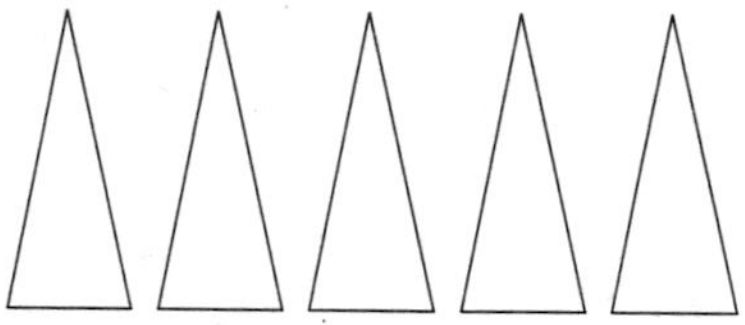 2 + 3 = ☐

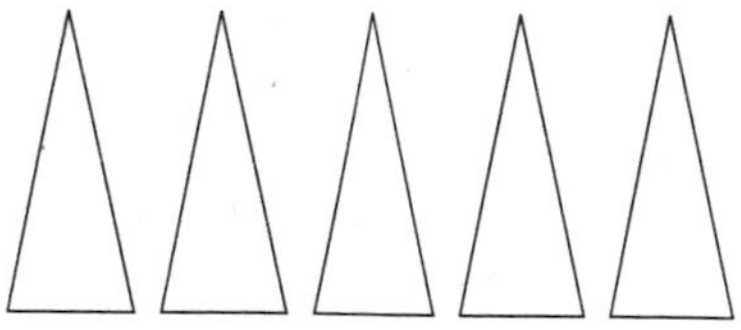 + 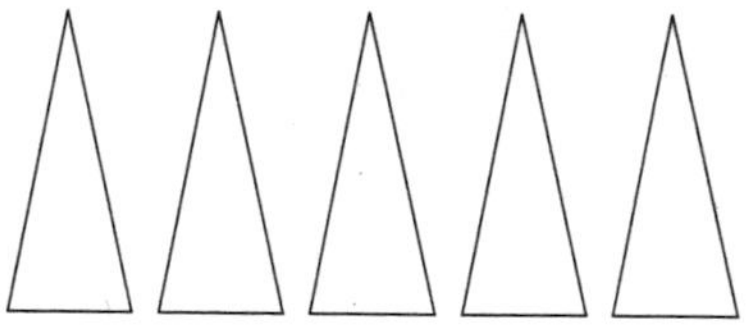 1 + 0 = ☐

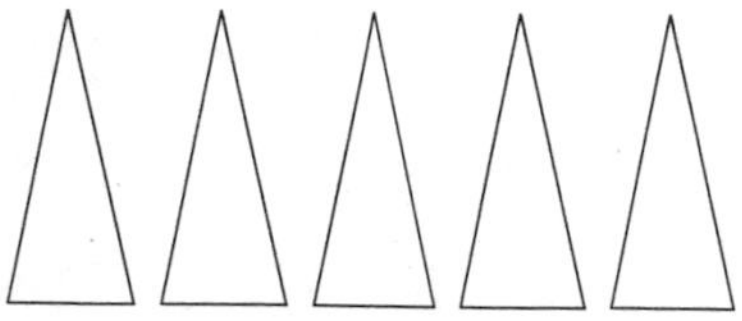 + 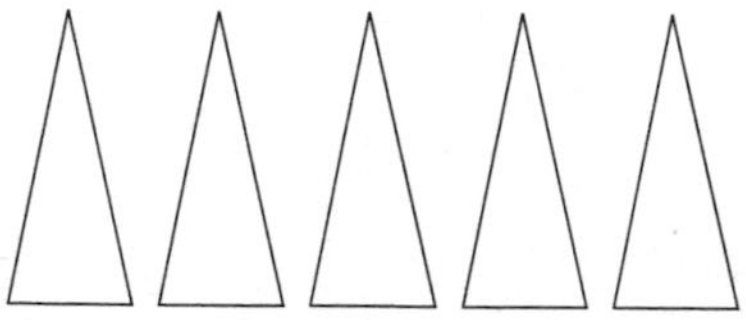 3 + 1 = ☐

Name: ______________________________ Date: ____________________

1.  count **2.** 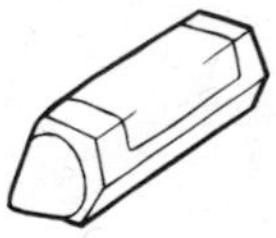 color **3.** 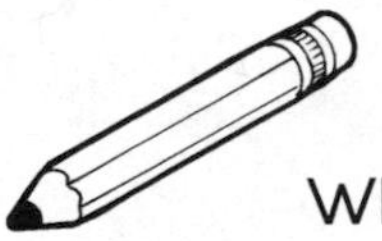 write

 +  2 + 2 = ☐

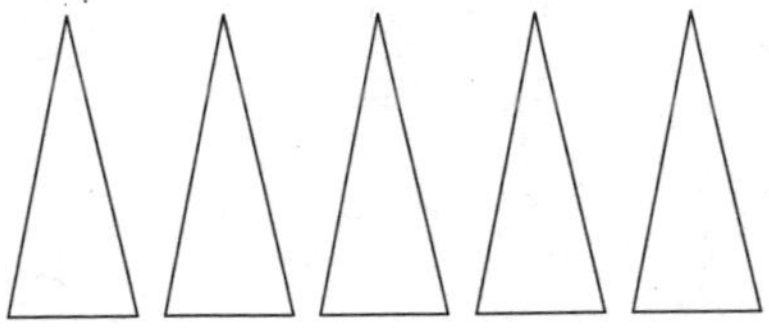 + 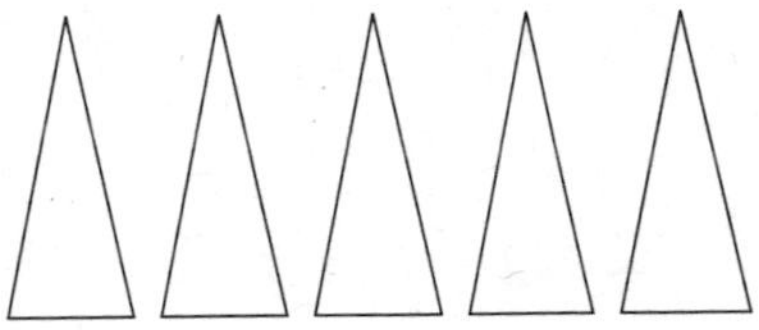 2 + 1 = ☐

 +  0 + 3 = ☐

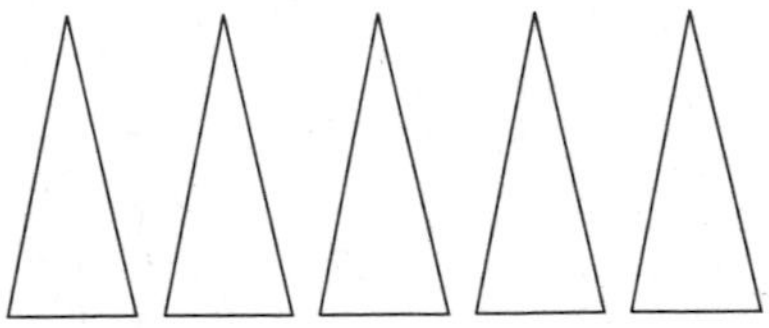 + 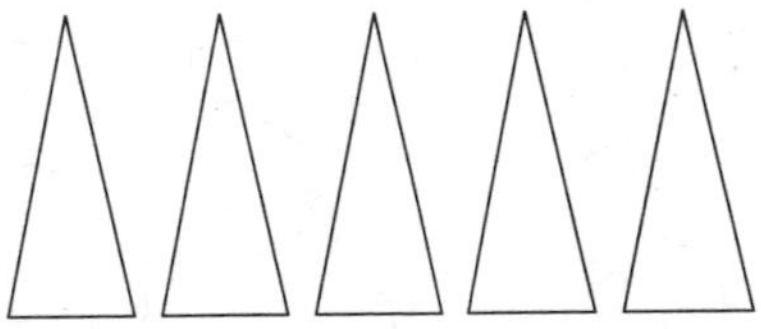 1 + 3 = ☐

 +  0 + 4 = ☐

Name: ______________________________ Date: ____________________

1.  count

2.  write

3.  color

 +  3 + 2 = 5

 +  ______ + ______ = ☐

 +  ______ + ______ = ☐

 +  ______ + ______ = ☐

 +  ______ + ______ = ☐

 +  ______ + ______ = ☐

Name: ______________________________ Date: ____________________

1.  count **2.**  write **3.** 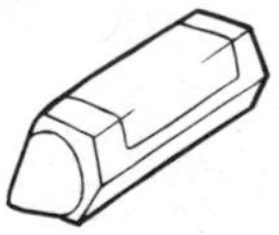 color

 +  _____ + _____ = ☐

 +  _____ + _____ = ☐

 +  _____ + _____ = ☐

 +  _____ + _____ = ☐

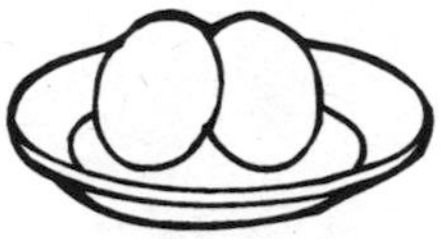 + 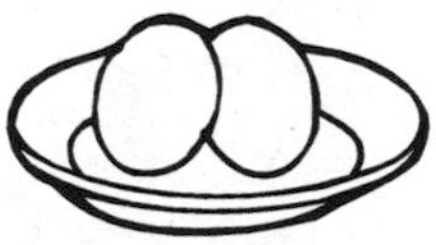 _____ + _____ = ☐

 +  _____ + _____ = ☐

Name: ______________________ Date: ______________________

1.  count **2.** 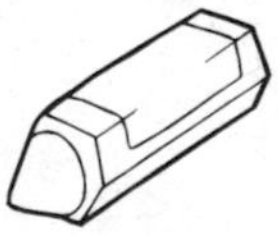 color **3.**  write

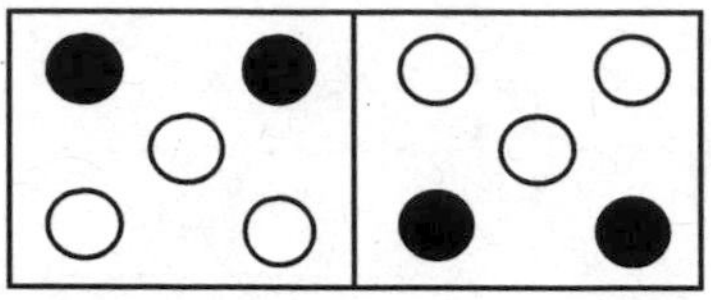

2 + 2 = 4

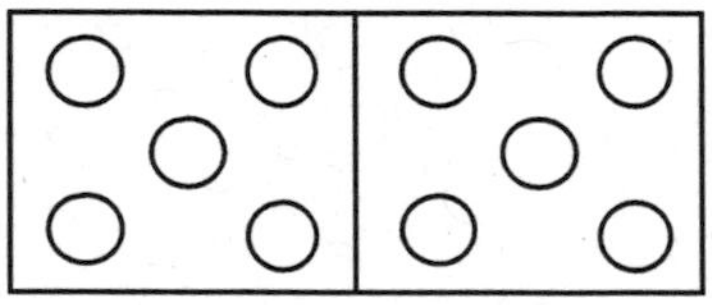

2 + 3 =

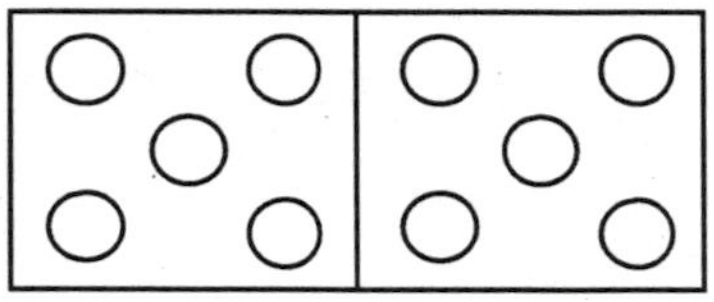

1 + 2 =

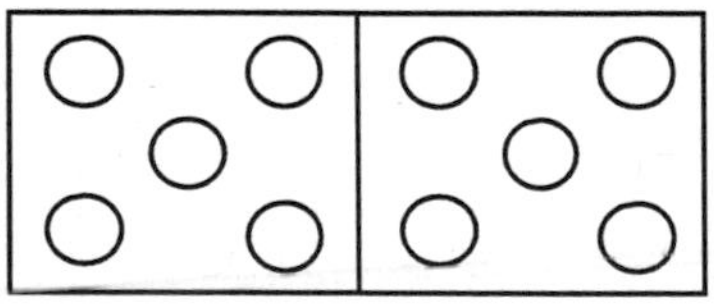

1 + 1 =

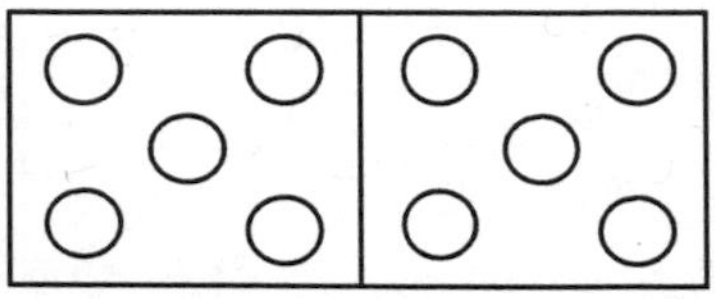

1 + 3 =

Name: ____________________ Date: ____________________

1.  count **2.** 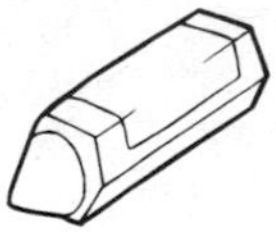 color **3.**  write

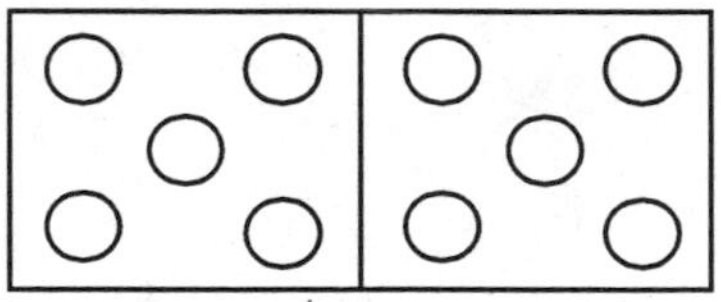

4 + 1 =

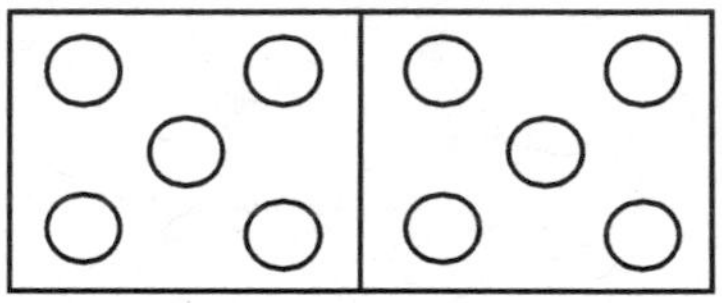

0 + 5 =

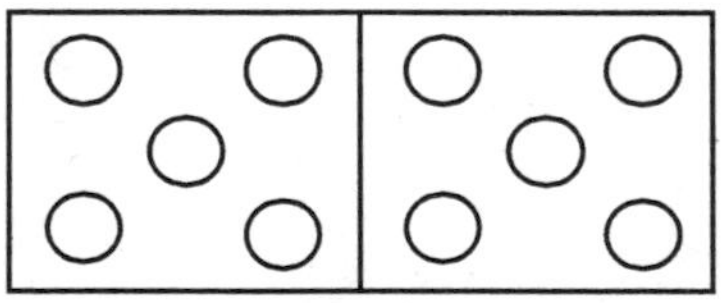

3 + 1 =

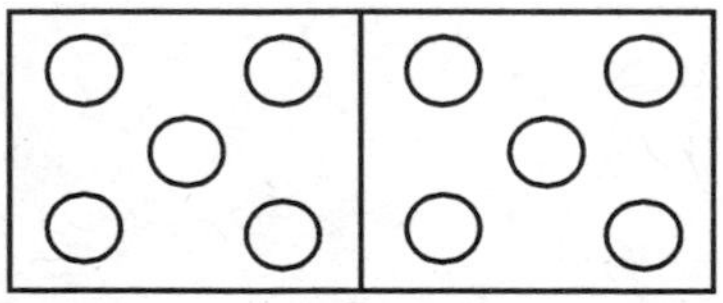

4 + 0 =

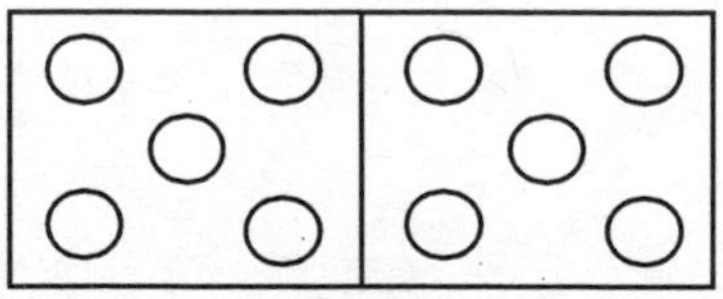

5 + 0 =

Name: ______________________ Date: ______________

1.  draw **2.** 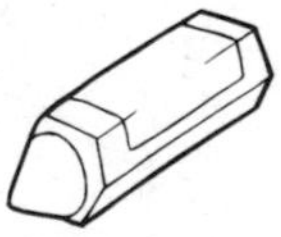 color **3.**  count **4.**  write

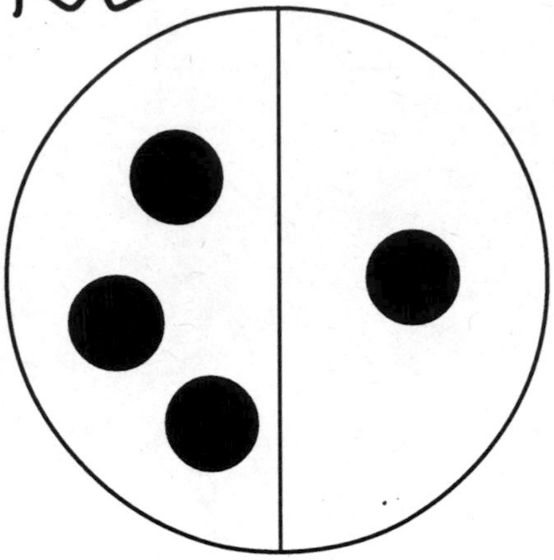

3 + 1 = ________

1 + 2 = ________

1 + 4 = ________

2 + 2 = ________

1 + 3 = ________

2 + 0 = ________

Name: ______________________ Date: ______________________

1. 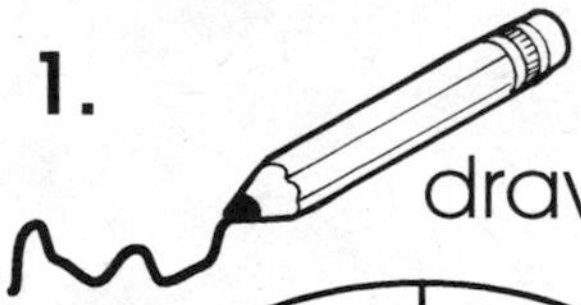 draw **2.** 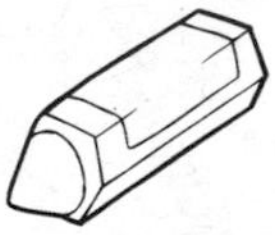 color **3.**  count **4.**  write

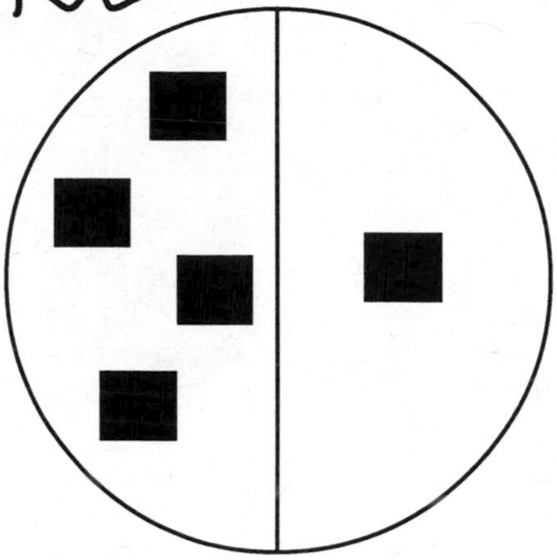

4 + 1 = ________

2 + 3 = ________

5 + 0 = ________

2 + 2 = ________

3 + 1 = ________

1 + 2 = ________

Name: ______________________ Date: ______________

1. 

count 2.  write 3. 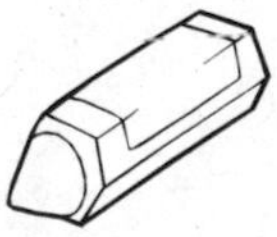 color

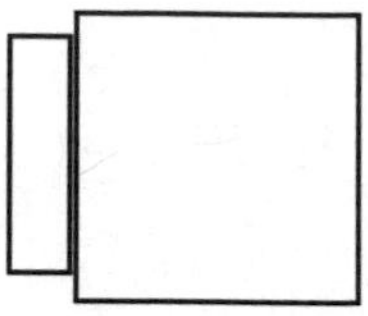 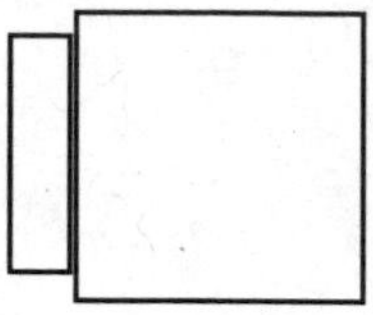

1 + 1 = 2

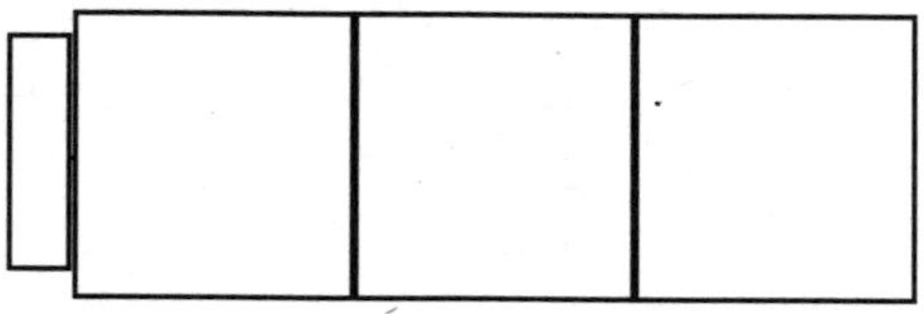 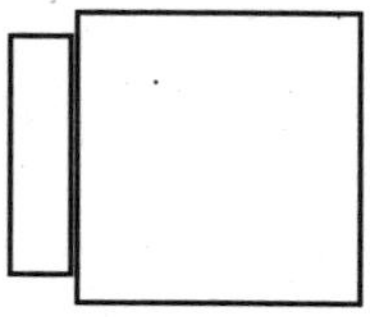

______ + ______ = ______

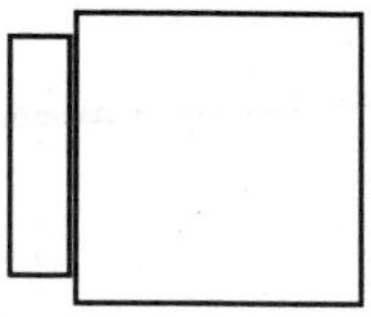 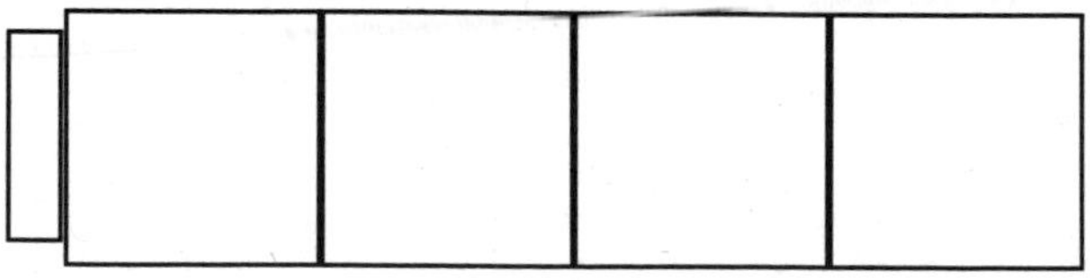

______ + ______ = ______

Name: ______________________ Date: ______________

1.  count 2. 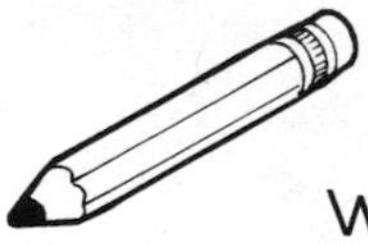 write 3. 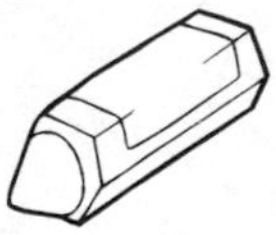 color

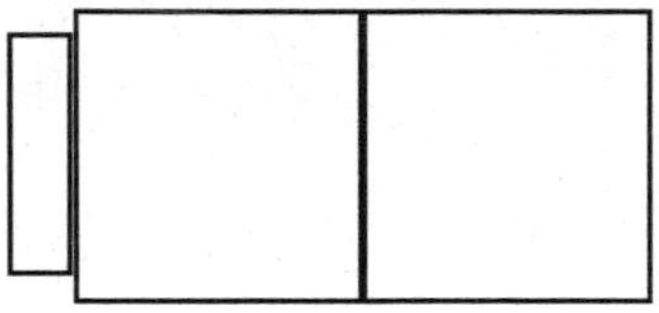 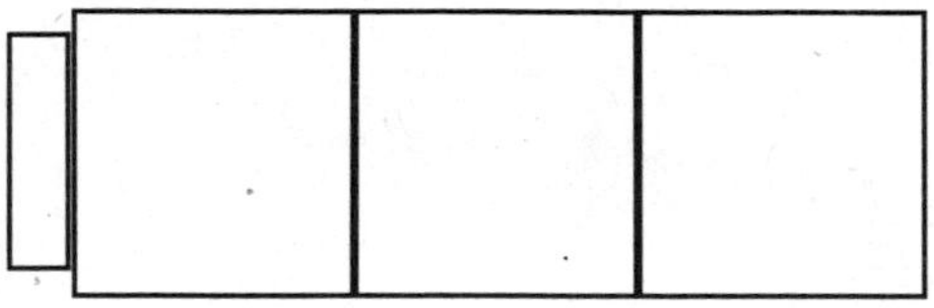

____ + ____ = ____

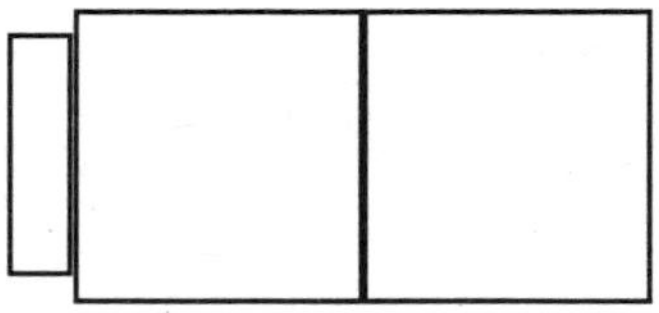 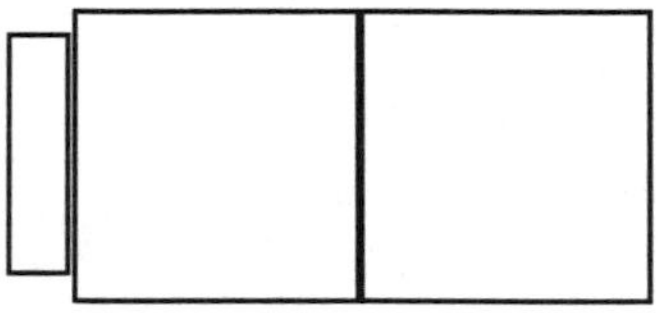

____ + ____ = ____

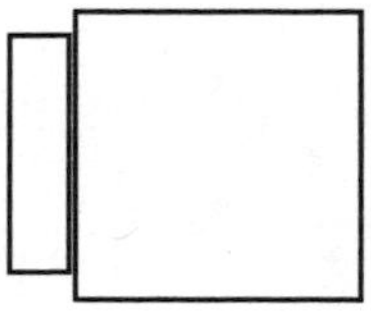 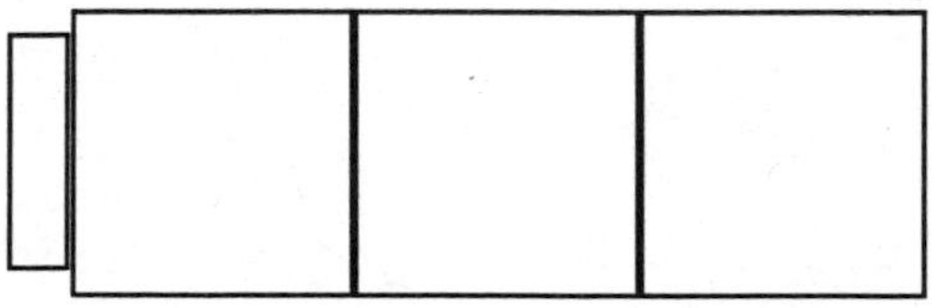

____ + ____ = ____

Name: ______________________ Date: ________________

1. add **2.** write **3.** color

1	green
2	yellow
3	blue
4	orange
5	red

2
+ 0
2

1
+ 4

1
+ 2

2
+ 2

0
+ 5

4
+ 1

1
+ 3

4
+ 0

3
+ 2

2
+ 2

0
+ 5

1
+ 1

Name: ______________________ Date: ______________

1. ✚ add **2.** write **3.** color ☐

1	–	purple
2	–	red
3	–	orange
4	–	blue
5	–	green

1 + 1 = ___	0 + 4 = ___	1 + 4 = ___	2 + 1 = ___	5 + 0 = ___
3 + 2 = ___	2 + 0 = ___	1 + 3 = ___	0 + 3 = ___	1 + 0 = ___
2 + 3 = ___	0 + 5 = ___	1 + 2 = ___	4 + 1 = ___	3 + 0 = ___
	2 + 2 = ___	3 + 1 = ___	3 + 1 = ___	0 + 1 = ___

Name: ______________________________ Date: ____________________

1. ✚ add **2.** 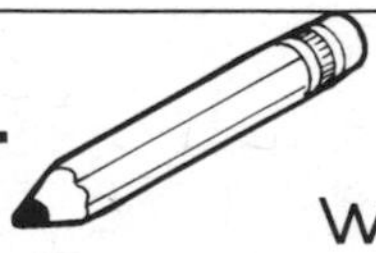 write **3.** 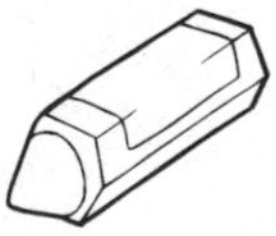 color

1	- green
2	- yellow
3	- blue
4	- orange
5	- red

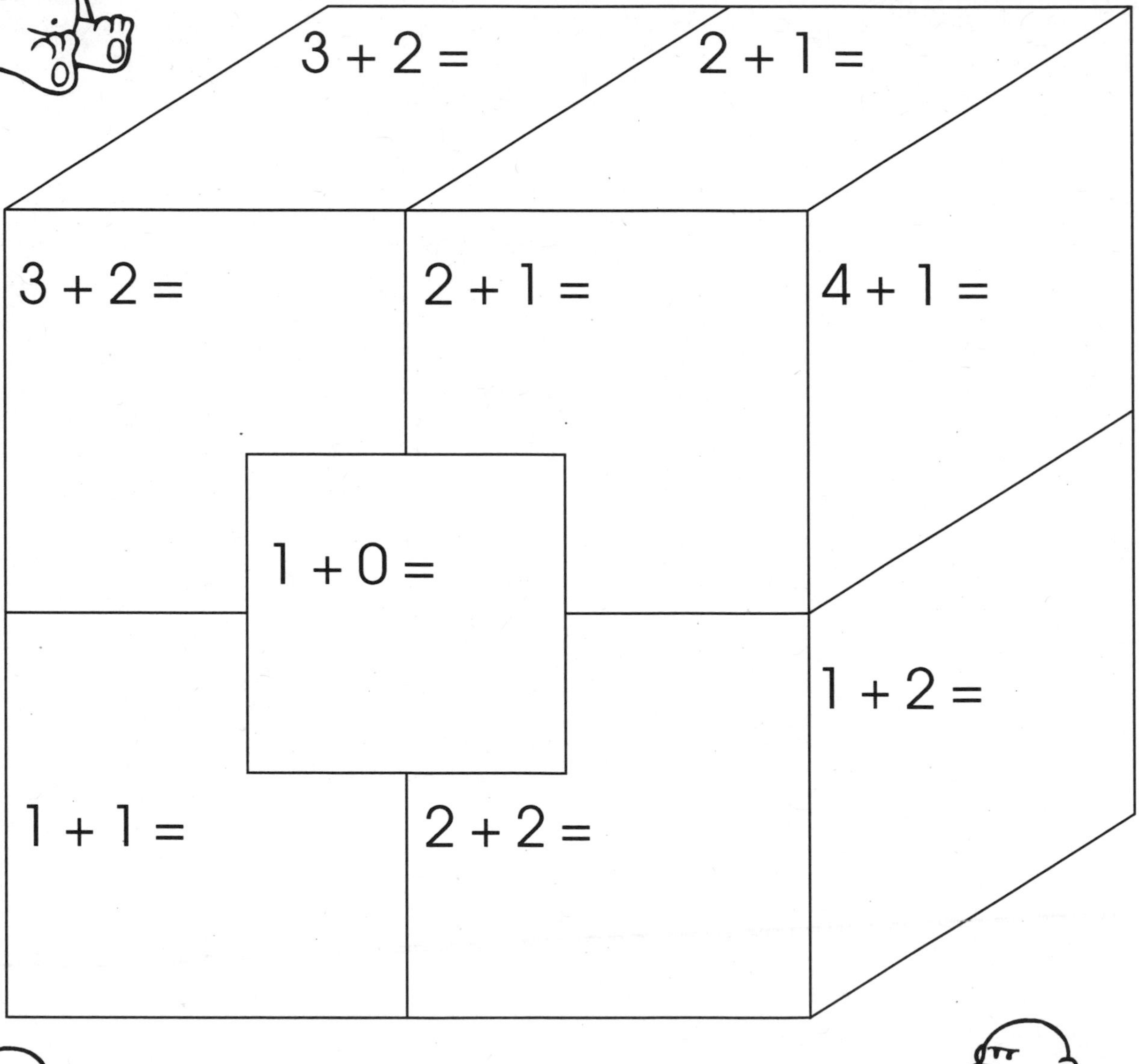

3 + 2 =
2 + 1 =
3 + 2 =
2 + 1 =
4 + 1 =
1 + 0 =
1 + 2 =
1 + 1 =
2 + 2 =

Name: ______________________ Date: ______________

1. 

count

2.  write

3.  color

5 + 0 = 5

____ + ____ =

____ + ____ =

____ + ____ =

____ + ____ =

Name: ______________________ Date: ______________________

1.  count 2. 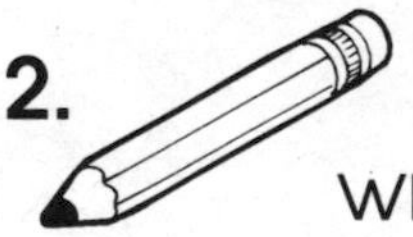 write 3. 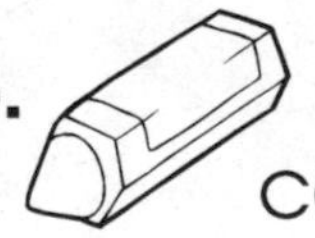 color

______ + ______ = ☐

______ + ______ = ☐

______ + ______ = ☐

______ + ______ = ☐

______ + ______ = ☐

Name: ______________________________ Date: ____________________

1.  count 2. 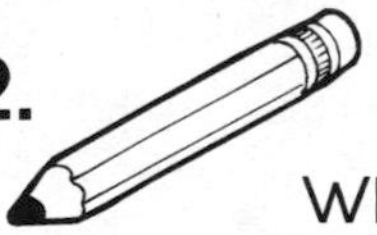 write 3.  color

3 + 0 = 3

_____ + _____ =

_____ + _____ =

_____ + _____ =

_____ + _____ =

_____ + _____ =

_____ + _____ =

_____ + _____ =

_____ + _____ =

_____ + _____ =

Name: ______________________________ Date: ____________________

1. ✚ add 2.  write 3. 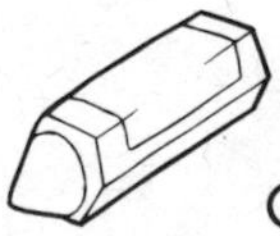 color

$2 + 2 =$	$4 + 1 =$	$2 + 0 =$
$1 + 1 =$	$4 + 0 =$	$0 + 5 =$
$1 + 2 =$	$1 + 0 =$	$2 + 3 =$
$1 + 3 =$	$3 + 0 =$	$3 + 2 =$
$0 + 5 =$	$1 + 4 =$	$5 + 0 =$

Name: ______________________________ Date: ____________________

1. add 2. write 3. color

2	–	orange
3	–	yellow
4	–	green
5	–	red

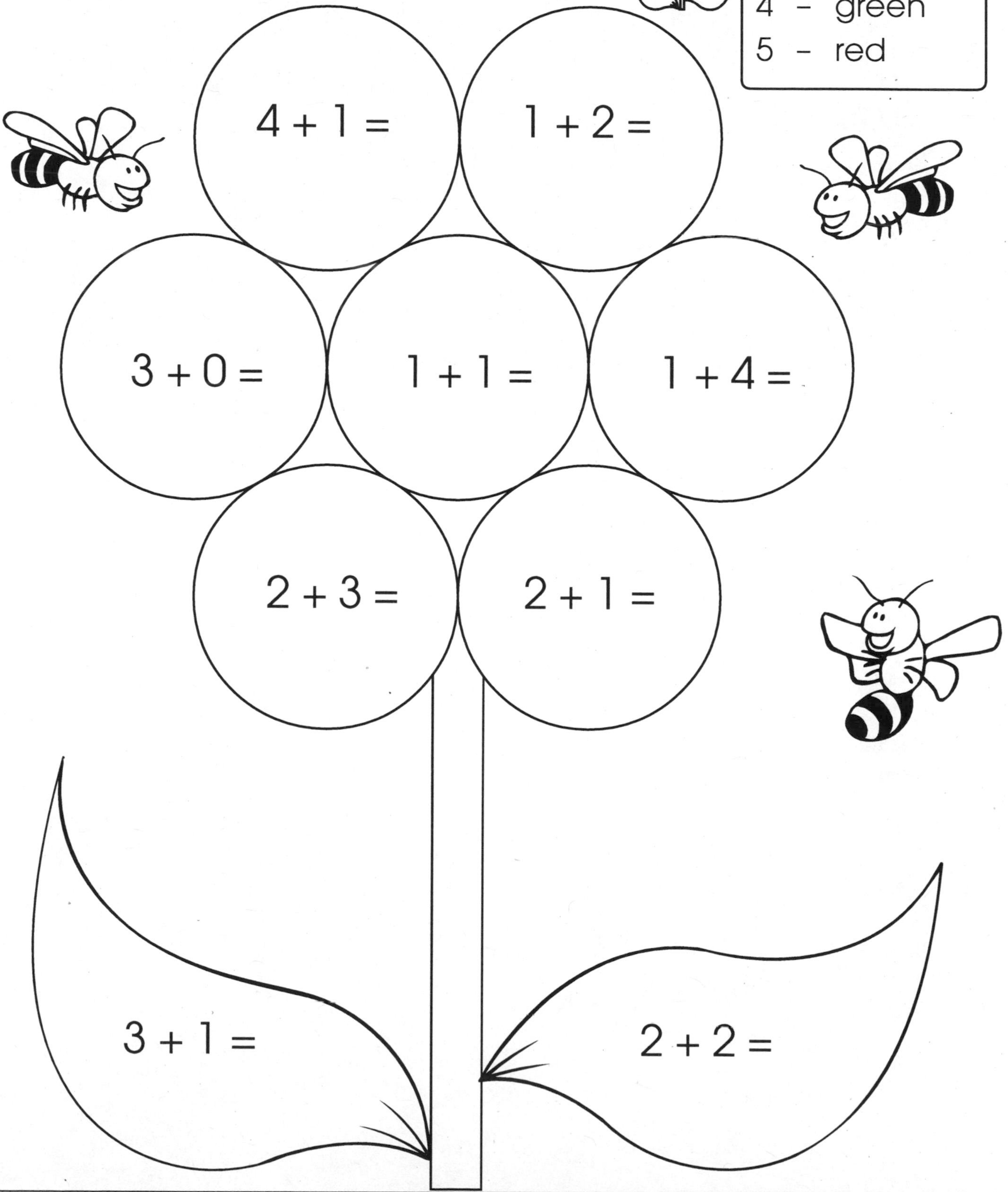

4 + 1 =
1 + 2 =
3 + 0 =
1 + 1 =
1 + 4 =
2 + 3 =
2 + 1 =
3 + 1 =
2 + 2 =

Name: ______________________ Date: ______________

1.  count **2.** 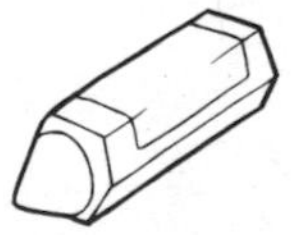 color **3.**  write

4 + 1 = ___

1 + 3 = ___

1 + 1 = ___

Name: ______________________ Date: ______________

1.  count **2.** 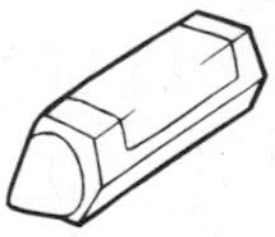 color **3.**  write

2 + 2 = ___

2 + 3 = ___

5 + 0 = ___

Name: ______________________________ Date: ____________________

1. + add **2.**  write

3 + 2 = ☐ 4 + 1 = ☐

1 + 0 = ☐ 1 + 3 = ☐

2 + 2 = ☐ 2 + 3 = ☐

1 + 1 = ☐ 2 + 1 = ☐

Name: ______________________ Date: ______________

1. add **2.** 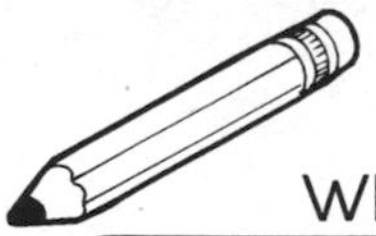 write

1 + 1 = ☐

1 + 2 = ☐

3 + 2 = ☐

1 + 0 = ☐

1 + 3 = ☐

4 + 1 = ☐

2 + 1 = ☐

0 + 3 = ☐

2 + 2 = ☐

3 + 1 = ☐

2 + 3 = ☐

1 + 4 = ☐

Name: ______________________________ Date: ____________________

1. ✚ add **2.**  write

$2 + 1 = \square$	$4 + 1 = \square$
$3 + 2 = \square$	$1 + 3 = \square$
$4 + 0 = \square$	$1 + 2 = \square$
$1 + 1 = \square$	$2 + 3 = \square$
$0 + 5 = \square$	$3 + 0 = \square$
$2 + 2 = \square$	$1 + 4 = \square$

Name: ______________________ Date: ______________________

1. add **2.** write

3 + 0	0 + 4	1 + 2	4 + 0
0 + 2	1 + 3	2 + 0	2 + 2
3 + 0	3 + 2	4 + 0	3 + 1
4 + 1	2 + 1	0 + 1	1 + 4
1 + 1	0 + 5	2 + 3	

Name: ______________________ Date: ______________________

1. add 2. write 3. cut 4. glue

3	4	5
2 + 1 =		

3 + 1 =	2 + 1 =	5 + 0 =	0 + 4 =
1 + 2 =	4 + 0 =	4 + 1 =	3 + 2 =
3 + 0 =	0 + 3 =	2 + 2 =	2 + 3 =

Name: ______________________ Date: ________________

1. ✚ add **2.**  write **3.** cut  **4.**  glue

3	4	5

3 + 2 =	3 + 1 =	0 + 3 =
0 + 5 =	0 + 4 =	4 + 1 =
2 + 2 =	1 + 2 =	4 + 0 =
2 + 3 =	3 + 0 =	2 + 1 =

Name: ______________________________ Date: ____________________

A sample page from the book, *Early Visual Skills,* also in the *Early Skills Series.*

1. 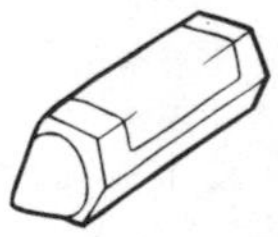 color **2.** cut  **3.**  glue